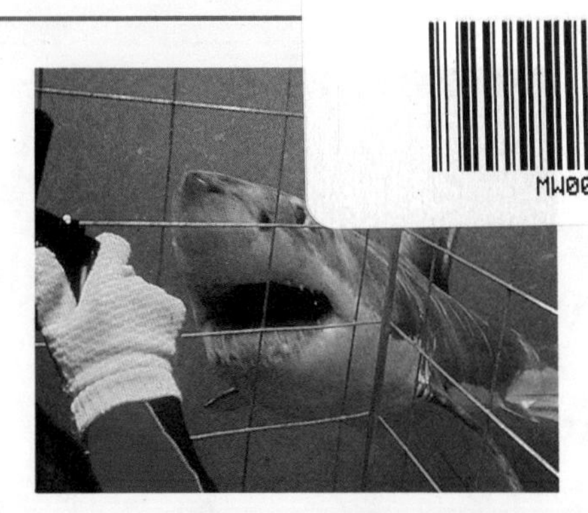

SHARKS

FACTS & PHOTOS

Edited by Jill Wolf

Photo Credits: Cover Photo by Jeff Rotman; Title Page Photo and Sand Shark (Grey Nurse) Sticker Photo by Ron & Valerie Taylor/Bruce Coleman, Inc. All other credits listed with photos.

ISBN 0-89954-129-1
Made in the United States of America

Antioch Publishing Company
Yellow Springs, Ohio 45387

NAME: **Great White Shark**

LENGTH: 20-36 feet

HOME: Atlantic, Pacific, and Indian Oceans

FAVORITE FOOD: fish, seals, sea lions, whales, turtles, rays, skates, other sharks

UNUSUAL FEATURES: The great white is one of the biggest and most dangerous sharks. Its teeth are 3 inches long! It takes giant bites-- as much as a 15-pound chunk of meat. Unlike other sharks, the great white gives no warning of attack. It is a known man-eater.

Photo by Carl Roessler/Bruce Coleman, Inc.

NAME: **Hammerhead Shark**

LENGTH: 14-20 feet

HOME: Atlantic and Pacific Oceans, Caribbean Sea

FAVORITE FOOD: fish, other sharks, sting rays

UNUSUAL FEATURES: A hammerhead's eyes and nostrils are on the ends of its odd-shaped head. Hammerheads often hunt in packs. Humans used to hunt them for their livers, which are rich in oil and vitamin A. These sharks will attack humans and like to eat sting rays. The ray's poison stingers don't seem to hurt them!

Photo by John S. Flannery/Bruce Coleman, Inc.

NAME: **Blue Shark**

LENGTH: 7-20 feet

HOME: warm seas and coasts worldwide

FAVORITE FOOD: fish, whale meat, squid

UNUSUAL FEATURES: The blue shark is beautiful and can swim very fast-- about 35 miles per hour! Because it likes to eat a whaling boat's catch, it is called the blue "whaler." Even if the whaling crew hits it over the head, it won't stop eating. Blue sharks also attack humans.

Photo by Ron & Valerie Taylor/Bruce Coleman, Inc.

NAME: **Sand Tiger Shark**

LENGTH: 10 feet

HOME: Atlantic, Australian, South African, and Mediterranean coasts

FAVORITE FOOD: fish, octopuses, squid, lobsters, crabs, other sharks

UNUSUAL FEATURES: The sand tiger shark is famous for being a cannibal (eating its own kind). When it is a pup (baby), it eats the unhatched eggs of its brothers and sisters. Even as a pup, this fierce shark will bite a human. It is known in Australia for attacks on swimmers.

Photo by Jeff Rotman

NAME: **White-Tip Shark**

LENGTH: 5-13 feet

HOME: Pacific and Indian Oceans, Red Sea

FAVORITE FOOD: fish, other sharks

UNUSUAL FEATURES: White-tip sharks will attack swimmers, divers, and shipwrecked people. These savage sharks are known for feeding frenzy. They get so excited, they bite and tear at everything-- their food, boat propellers, or each other. Even when hit by bullets, they keep attacking!

Photo by Ron & Valerie Taylor/Bruce Coleman, Inc.

NAME: **Lemon Shark**

LENGTH: 8-11 feet

HOME: Atlantic Ocean, Caribbean Sea, and eastern Pacific Ocean

FAVORITE FOOD: sting rays, octopuses, sea birds, fish, lobsters, crabs, shrimp

UNUSUAL FEATURES: Although the lemon shark is dangerous, it does well in captivity. It can learn how to tell shapes apart and how to hit a target for a food reward. Its name comes from the yellowish-brown color of its skin. The lemon shark is often found with sting ray spines or stingers stuck in its jaws.

Photo by Fred Whitehead/ANIMALS, ANIMALS

NAME: **Carpet Shark (Wobbegong)**

LENGTH: 6-10 feet

HOME: reefs of Australia, Southeast Asia, China, and Japan

FAVORITE FOOD: crayfish, lobsters, shrimp, crabs, fish

UNUSUAL FEATURES: The carpet shark is the king of camouflage. With its dull colors, spots, and tassels of skin, it blends right into the ocean floor. Carpet sharks are sluggish and harmless, unless they are attacked or stepped on. Humans hunt them for their skins, which make good leather.

Photo by A. Power/Bruce Coleman, Inc.

NAME: **Leopard Shark**

LENGTH: 5-6 feet

HOME: Pacific coast of North America

FAVORITE FOOD: octopuses, clams, crabs, lobsters, small fish, fish eggs

UNUSUAL FEATURES: The leopard shark takes its name from the cat-like spots and stripes on its back. It has many small teeth, but it is harmless and does well in captivity. Leopard sharks are common along the coast from Oregon to Mexico. They especially like to eat clams.

Photo by L.L.T. Rhodes/ANIMALS, ANIMALS

NAME: **Epaulette Shark**

LENGTH: 3-4 feet

HOME: western Pacific reefs, especially the Great Barrier Reef of Australia

FAVORITE FOOD: small fish, shrimp, lobsters, clams, crabs

UNUSUAL FEATURES: The spotted epaulette shark is a beautiful and harmless relative of the carpet shark. It is so "tame," it will hunt for food at a diver's feet. Muscular paired fins help this shark move across the reefs where it lives.

Photo by A. Power/Bruce Coleman, Inc.

NAME: **Bonnethead Shark**

LENGTH: 5 feet

HOME: western Atlantic and eastern Pacific coasts

FAVORITE FOOD: small fish, crabs, shrimp, squid

UNUSUAL FEATURES: The flat, rounded head of this shark gives it its funny name. (It is also called the shovelhead.) Like the closely related hammerhead sharks, bonnetheads have large brains. They gather in small groups of 20 or more, and use body movements or "language" to communicate.

Photo by Zig Leszczynski/ANIMALS, ANIMALS

NAME: **Zebra Shark**

LENGTH: 10 feet

HOME: western Pacific Ocean and the Indian Ocean

FAVORITE FOOD: crabs, lobsters, shrimp, barnacles, clams, snails

UNUSUAL FEATURES: The zebra shark starts out with stripes that turn to spots when it becomes an adult. Because of these spots, it is also called the leopard shark. It is not harmful to man, but is often hunted for its skin. The zebra shark's tail is so long, it makes up half of the shark's total length!

Photo by Ron & Valerie Taylor/Bruce Coleman, Inc.

Shark Trivia

Q. How long have sharks lived on earth?

A. As early as 350 million years ago -- even ***before*** *the dinosaurs!*

Q. What is the biggest living shark?

A. The whale shark is the biggest; it is 50 feet long and weighs 15 tons.

Q. Does a shark have to eat every day?

A. No, it can go for months without a meal because it lives off the fat in its liver.

Q. How many bones does a shark have?

A. None. A shark's skeleton is made of cartilage like the soft "bony" parts in your nose.

Q. What is the smallest living shark?

A. The tsuranagakobitozame is the smallest; it is 4-5 inches long.

Q. How many times do sharks chew their food?

A. They don't chew their food -- they swallow it whole.

Q. Which shark seems friendly to man?

A. The whale shark is so gentle that divers often take rides on it.